I'm Reading Now!

Ben Gets Ready for School

by Shelley Harwayne
Illustrated by Jannie Ho

SCHOLASTIC INC.
New York   Toronto   London   Auckland   Sydney
Mexico City   New Delhi   Hong Kong   Buenos Aires

ISBN-13: 978-0-545-07057-7
ISBN-10: 0-545-07057-0

Text copyright © 2008 by Shelley Harwayne
Illustrations copyright © 2008 by Jannie Ho

12 11 10 9 8 7 6 5 4 3 2   8 9 10 11 12 13/0

Printed in the U.S.A.
First printing, September 2008

Mommy says, "It's raining."
Ben gets his umbrella.

Mommy says, "Now it's sunny."

Ben gets his sunglasses.

Mommy says, "It's freezing."

Ben gets his scarf.

Mommy says, "It's Saturday."
Ben gets back into bed.